THE PLAIN MAN AND HIS WIFE

BY

ARNOLD BENNETT

AUTHOR OF "THE OLD WIVES' TALE," "CLAYHANGER,"
"HILDA LESSWAYS," ETC.

HODDER AND STOUGHTON

LONDON   NEW YORK   TORONTO

CONTENTS

CHAPTER I

CHAPTER I
ALL MEANS AND NO END

CHAPTER I

ALL MEANS AND NO END

I

THE plain man on a plain day wakes up, slowly or quickly according to his temperament, and greets the day in a mental posture which might be thus expressed in words :

" Oh, Lord ! Another day ! What a grind ! "

If you ask me whom I mean by the plain man, my reply is that I mean almost every man. I mean you. I certainly mean me. I mean the rich and the poor, the successful and the unsuccessful, the idle and the diligent, the

luxurious and the austere. For, what
with the limits of digestion, the practical
impossibility of wearing two neckties at
once, the insecurity of investments, the
responsibilities of wealth and of success,
the exhaustingness of the search for
pleasure, and the cheapness of travel—
the real differences between one sort of
plain man and another are slight in these
times. (And indeed they always were
slight.)

The plain man has a lot to do before he
may have his breakfast—and he must do
it. The tyrannic routine begins instantly
he is out of bed. To lave limbs, to shave
the jaw, to select clothes and assume
them—these things are naught. He must
exercise his muscles—all his muscles
equally and scientifically—with the aid
of a text-book and of diagrams on a large
card ; which card he often hides if he is
expecting visitors in his chamber, for he

will not always confess to these exercises ;
he would have you believe that he alone,
in a world of simpletons, is above the
faddism of the hour ; he is as ashamed
of these exercises as of a good resolution,
and when his wife happens to burst in
on them he will pretend to be doing some
common act, such as walking across the
room or examining a mole in the small
of his back. And yet he will not abandon
them. They have an empire over him.
To drop them would be to be craven,
inefficient. The text-book asserts that
they will form one of the pleasantest
parts of the day, and that he will learn
to look forward to them. He soon learns
to look forward to them, but not with
glee. He is relieved and proud when
they are over for the day.

He would enjoy his breakfast, thanks
to the strenuous imitation of diagrams,
were it not that, in addition to being

generally in a hurry, he is preoccupied. He is preoccupied by the sense of doom, by the sense that he has set out on the appointed path and dare not stray from it. The train or the tram-car or the automobile (same thing) is waiting for him, irrevocable, undeniable, inevitable. He wrenches himself away. He goes forth to his fate, as to the dentist. And just as he would enjoy his breakfast in the home, so he would enjoy his newspaper and cigarette in the vehicle, were it not for that ever-present sense of doom. The idea of business grips him. It matters not what the business is. Business is everything, and everything is business. He reaches his office—whatever his office is. He is in his office. He must plunge —he plunges. The day has genuinely begun now. The appointed path stretches straight in front of him, for five, six, seven, eight hours.

Oh! but he chose his vocation. He likes it. It satisfies his instincts. It is his life. (So you say.) Well, does he like it? Does it satisfy his instincts? Is it his life? If truly the answer is affirmative, he is at any rate not conscious of the fact. He is aware of no ecstasy. What is the use of being happy unless he knows he is happy? Some men know that they are happy in the hours of business, but they are few. The majority are not, and the bulk of the majority do not even pretend to be. The whole attitude of the average plain man to business implies that business is a nuisance, scarcely mitigated. With what secret satisfaction he anticipates that visit to the barber's in the middle of the morning! With what gusto he hails the arrival of an unexpected interrupting friend! With what easement he decides that he may lawfully put off some task till the morrow! Let him hear a band or a fire-engine in the street, and he will go to the window with the eagerness of a child or of a girl-clerk. If he were working at golf the bands of all the regiments of Hohenzollern would not make him turn his head, nor the multitudinous blazing of fireproof skyscrapers. No! Let us be honest. Business constitutes the steepest, roughest league of the appointed path. Were it otherwise, business would not be universally regarded as a means to an end.

Moreover, when the plain man gets home again, does his wife's face say to him : " I know that your real life is now over for the day, and I regret for your sake that you have to return here. I know that the powerful interest of your life is gone. But I am glad that you have had five, six, seven, or eight hours of passionate pleasure " ? Not a bit!

His wife's face says to him : " I com-
miserate with you on all that you have
been through. It is a great shame that
you should be compelled to toil thus
painfully. But I will try to make it up
to you. I will soothe you. I will humour
you. Forget anxiety and fatigue in my
smiles." She does not fetch his comfortable slippers for him, partly because, in
this century, wives do not do such things,
and partly because comfortable slippers
are no longer worn. But she does the
equivalent—whatever the equivalent may
happen to be in that particular household.
And he expects the commiseration and
the solace in her face. He would be
very hurt did he not find it there.

And even yet he is not relaxed. Even
yet the appointed path stretches in-
exorably in front, and he cannot wander.
For now he feels the cogs and cranks of
the highly complex domestic machine.

At breakfast he declined to hear them ;
they were shut off from him ; he was too
busy to be bothered with them. At
evening he must be bothered with them.
Was it not he who created the machine ?
He discovers, often to his astonishment,
that his wife has an existence of her own,
full of factors foreign to him, and he has
to project himself, not only into his wife's
existence, but into the existences of other
minor personages. His daughter, for example, will persist in growing up. Not
for a single day will she pause. He
arrives one night and perceives that she
is a woman and that he must treat her
as a woman. He had not bargained for
this. Peace, ease, relaxation in a home
vibrating to the whir of such astounding
phenomena ? Impossible dream ! These
phenomena were originally meant by him
to be the ornamentation of his career,
but they are threatening to be the sole

reason of his career. If his wife lives for him, it is certain that he lives just as much for his wife ; and as for his daughter, while she emphatically does not live for him, he is bound to admit that he has just got to live for her—and she knows it !

To gain money was exhausting; to spend it is precisely as exhausting. He cannot quit the appointed path nor lift the doom. Dinner is finished ere he has begun to recover from the varied shock of home. Then his daughter may negligently throw him a few moments of charming cajolery. He may gossip in simple idleness with his wife. He may gambol like any infant with the dog. A yawn. The shadow of the next day is upon him. He must not stay up too late, lest the vigour demanded by the next day should be impaired. Besides, he does not want to stay up. Naught is quite interesting enough to keep him up. And bed, too, is part of the appointed, unescapable path. To bed he goes, carrying ten million preoccupations. And of his state of mind the kindest that can be said is that he is philosophic enough to hope for the best.

And after the night he wakes up, slowly or quickly according to his temperament, and greets the day with :

" Oh, Lord ! Another day ! What a grind ! "

The interesting point about the whole situation is that the plain man seldom or never asks himself a really fundamental question about that appointed path of his —that path from which he dare not and could not wander.

Once, perhaps in a parable, the plain man travelling met another traveller. And the plain man demanded of the traveller :

" Where are you going to ? "

The traveller replied :

" Now I come to think of it, I don't know."

The plain man was ruffled by this insensate answer. He said :

" But you *are* travelling ? "

The traveller replied :

" Yes."

The plain man, beginning to be annoyed, said :

" Have you never asked yourself where you are going to ? "

Said the traveller :

" I have not."

" But do you mean to tell me," protested the plain man, now irritated, " that you are putting yourself to all this trouble, peril, and expense of trains and steamers without having asked yourself where you are going to ? "

" It never occurred to me," the traveller admitted. " I just had to start and I started."

Whereupon the plain man was, as too often with us plain men, staggered and deeply affronted by the illogical absurdity of human nature. " Was it conceivable," he thought, " that this traveller, presumably in his senses——" etc. (You are familiar with the tone and the style, being a plain man yourself.) And he gave way to moral indignation.

Now I must here, in parenthesis, firmly state that I happen to be a member of the Society for the Suppression of Moral Indignation. As such, I object to the plain man's moral indignation against the traveller; and I think that a liability to moral indignation is one of the plain man's most serious defects. As such, my endeavour is to avoid being staggered and deeply affronted, or even surprised, by human vagaries. There are too many plain people who are always rediscovering human nature—its turpitudes, fatuities, unreason. They live amid human nature as in a chamber of horrors. And yet, after all these years, we surely ought to have grown used to human nature! It may be extremely vile—that

is not the point. The point is that it
constitutes our environment, from which
we cannot escape alive. The man who is
capable of being deeply affronted by his
inevitable environment ought to have
the pluck of his convictions and shoot
himself. The Society would with pleasure
pay his funeral expenses and contribute
to the support of his wife and children.
Such a man is, without knowing it, a dire
enemy of true progress, which can only
be planned and executed in an atmosphere from which heated moral superiority
is absent.

I offer these parenthetical remarks as a
guarantee that I shall not over-righteously
sneer at the plain man for his share in the
sequel to the conversation with the traveller. For there was a sequel to the
conversation.

" As questions are being asked, where
are *you* going to ? " said the traveller.

The plain man answered with assurance :

"Oh, I know exactly where I'm going to. I'm going to Timbuctoo."

"Indeed!" said the traveller. "And why are you going to Timbuctoo?"

Said the plain man : "I'm going because it's the proper place to go to. Every self-respecting person goes to Timbuctoo."

"But why?"

Said the plain man :

"Well, it's supposed to be just about unique. You're contented there. You get what you've always wanted. The climate's wonderful."

"Indeed!" said the traveller again. "Have you met anybody who's been there?"

"Yes, I've met several. I've met a lot. And I've heard from people who are there."

2

" And are their reports enthusiastic ? "

" Well——" The plain man hesitated.

" Answer me. Are their reports enthusiastic ? " the traveller insisted, rather bullyingly.

" Not very," the plain man admitted. " Some say it's very disappointing. And some say it's much like other towns. Every one says the climate has grave drawbacks."

The traveller demanded :

" Then why are you going there ? "

Said the plain man :

" It never occurred to me to ask why. As I say, Timbuctoo's supposed to be——"

" Supposed by whom ? "

" Well—generally supposed," said the plain man, limply.

" Not by the people who've been there ? " the traveller persevered, with obstinacy.

" Perhaps not," breathed the plain

man. " But it's generally supposed——"
He faltered.

There was a silence, which was broken
by the traveller, who inquired :

" Any interesting places *en route* ? "

" I don't know. I never troubled about
that," said the plain man.

" But do you mean to tell me," the
traveller exclaimed, " that you are putting
yourself to all this trouble, peril, and
expense of trains and steamers and camel-
back without having asked yourself why,
and without having satisfied yourself
that the thing was worth while, and without having even ascertained the most
agreeable route ? "

Said the plain man, weakly :

" I just had to start for somewhere, so
I started for Timbuctoo."

Said the traveller :

" Well, I'm of a forgiving disposition.
Shake hands."

The two individuals in the foregoing parable were worrying each other with fundamental questions. And what makes the parable unrealistic is the improbability of real individuals ever doing any such thing. If the plain man, for instance, has almost ceased to deal in fundamental questions in these days, the reason is not difficult to find. The reason lies in the modern perception that fundamental questions are getting very hard to answer. In a former time a dogmatic answer was ready waiting for every fundamental question. You asked the question, but before you asked it you knew the answer, and so there was no argument and nearly no anxiety. In that former time a mere child could glance at your conduct and tell you with certainty exactly what you would be doing and how you would be feeling ten thousand years hence, if you persisted in the said conduct. But knowledge has advanced since then, and the inconvenience of increased knowledge is that it intensifies the sense of ignorance, with the result that, though we know immensely more than our grandfathers knew, we feel immensely more ignorant than they ever felt. They were, indeed, too ignorant to be aware of ignorance— which is perhaps a comfortable state. Thus the plain man nowadays shirks fundamental questions. And assuredly no member of the Society for the Suppression of Moral Indignation shall blame him.

All fundamental questions resolve themselves finally into the following assertion and inquiry about life : " I am now engaged in something rather tiresome. What do I stand to gain by it later on ? " That is the basic query. It has forms of varying importance. In its supreme form the word " eternity " has to be employed. And the plain man is, to-day, so sensitive about this supreme form of the question that, far from asking and trying to answer it, he can scarcely bear to hear it even discussed—I mean discussed with candour. In practice a frank discussion of it usually tempts him to exhibitions of extraordinary heat and bitterness, and wisdom is thereby but obscured. Therefore he prefers the disadvantage of leaving it alone to the dissatisfaction of attempting to deal with it. The disadvantage of leaving it alone is obvious. Existence is, and must be, a compromise between the claims of the moment and the claims of the future— and how can that compromise be wisely

established if one has not somehow made
up one's mind about the future ? It
cannot. But—I repeat—I would not
blame the plain man. I would only just
hint to him, while respecting his sensitive-
ness, that the present hour is just as
much a part of eternity as another hour
ten thousand years off.

The second—the next most important
—form of the fundamental question em-
braces the problem of old age. All plain
men will admit, when faithfully cross-
examined, a sort of belief that they are
on their way to some Timbuctoo situate
in the region of old age. It may be the
Timbuctoo of a special ambition realized,
or the Timbuctoo of luxury, or the Timbuctoo of material security, or the Timbuctoo of hale health, or the Timbuctoo
of knowledge, or the Timbuctoo of power,
or even the Timbuctoo of a good con-
science. It is anyhow a recognizable and

definable Timbuctoo. And the path leading to it is a straight, wide thoroughfare, clearly visible for a long distance ahead.

The theory of the mortal journey is simple and seldom challenged. It is a twofold theory—first that the delight of achievement will compensate for the rigours and self-denials of the route, and second that the misery of non-achievement would outweigh the immediate pleasures of dallying. If this theory were not indestructible, for reasons connected with the secret nature of humanity, it would probably have been destroyed long ago by the mere cumulative battering of experience. For the earth's surface is everywhere thickly dotted with old men who have achieved ambition, old men drenched in luxury, old men as safe as Mont Blanc from overthrow, old men with the health of camels, old men who know more than anybody ever knew before, old men whose nod can ruin a thousand miles of railroad, and old men with consciences of pure snow ; but who are not happy and cannot enjoy life.

The theory, however, does happen to be indestructible, partly because old age is such a terrible long way off, partly because the young honestly believe themselves to have a monopoly of wisdom, partly because every plain man is convinced that his case will be different from all the other cases, and chiefly because endeavour—not any particular endeavour, but rather any endeavour !—is a habit that corresponds to a very profound instinct in the plain man. So the reputation of Timbuctoo as a pleasure resort remains entirely unimpaired, and the pilgrimages continue with unabated earnestness.

And there is another and a paramount

reason why the pilgrimages should continue. The two men in the parable both said that they just had to start—and they were right. We have to start, and, once started, we have to keep going. We must go somewhere. And at the moment of starting we have neither the sagacity nor the leisure to invent fresh places to start for, or to cut new paths. Everybody is going to Timbuctoo; the roads are well marked. And the plain man, with his horror of being peculiar, sets out for Timbuctoo also, following the signposts. The fear of not arriving keeps him on the trot, the fear of the unknown keeps him in the middle of the road and out of the forest on either side of it, and hope keeps up his courage.

Will any member of the Society for the Suppression of Moral Indignation step forward and heatedly charge the plain man with culpable foolishness, ignorance, or

gullibility ; or even with cowardice in
neglecting to find a convincing answer to
the fundamental question about the other
end of his life ?

IV

There is, however, a third form of the
fundamental question which is less un-
answerable than the two forms already
mentioned. The plain man may be ex-
cused for his remarkable indifference as
to what his labour and his tedium will
gain for him " later on," when " later on "
means beyond the grave or thirty years
hence. But we live also in the present,
and if proper existence is a compromise
between the claims of the present and the
claims of the future the present must
be considered, and the plain man ought
surely to ask himself the fundamental
question in such a form as the following :
" I am now—this morning—engaged in
something rather tiresome. What do I

stand to gain by it this evening, to-morrow, this week—next week ? " In this form the fundamental question, once put, can be immediately answered by experience and by experiment.

But does the plain man put it ? I mean—does he put it seriously and effectively ? I think that very often, if not as a general rule, he does not. He may —in fact he does—gloomily and savagely mutter : " What pleasure do I get out of life ? " But he fails to insist on a clear answer from himself, and even if he obtains a clear answer—even if he makes the candid admission, " No pleasure," or " Not enough pleasure "—even then he usually does not insist on modifying his life in accordance with the answer. He goes on ignoring all the interesting towns and oases on the way to his Timbuctoo. Excessively uncertain about future joy, and too breathlessly preoccupied to think about joy in the present, he just drives obstinately ahead, rather like a person in a trance. Singular conduct for a plain man priding himself on common sense !

For the case of the plain man, conscientious and able, can only too frequently be summed up thus : Faced with the problem of existence, which is the problem of combining the largest possible amount of present satisfaction with the largest possible amount of security in the future, he has educated himself generally, and he has educated himself specially for a particular profession or trade ; he has adopted the profession or trade, with all its risks and responsibilities—risks and responsibilities which often involve the felicity of others ; he has bound himself to it for life, almost irrevocably ; he labours for it so many hours a day, and it occupies his thoughts for so many hours more. Further, in the quest of satisfaction, he has taken a woman to wife and has had children. And here it is well to note frankly that his prime object in marrying was not the woman's happiness, but his own, and that the children came, not in order that they might be jolly little creatures, but as extensions of the father's individuality. The home, the environment gradually constructed for these secondary beings, constitutes another complex organization, which he superimposes on the complex organization of his profession or trade, and his brain has to carry and vitalize the two of them. All his energies are absorbed, and they are absorbed so utterly that once a year he is obliged to take a holiday lest he should break down, and even the organization of the holiday is complex and exhausting.

Now assuming—a tremendous assumption!—that by all this he really is providing security for the future, what conscious direct, personal satisfaction in the present does the onerous programme actually yield ? I admit that it yields the primitive satisfaction of keeping body and soul together. But a Hottentot in a kraal gets the same satisfaction at less expense. I admit also that it ought theoretically to yield the conscious satisfaction which accompanies any sustained effort of the faculties. I deny that in fact it does yield this satisfaction, for the reason that the man is too busy ever to examine the treasures of his soul. And what else does it yield ? For what other immediate end is the colossal travail being accomplished ?

Well, it may, and does, occur that the plain man is practising physical and intellectual calisthenics, and running a vast business and sending ships and men to the horizons of the earth, and keeping

a home in a park, and oscillating like a
rapid shuttle daily between office and
home, and lying awake at nights, and
losing his eyesight and his digestion, and
staking his health, and risking misery for
the beings whom he cherishes, and en-
riching insurance companies, and providing
joy-rides for nice young women whom he
has never seen—and all his present profit
therefrom ·is a game of golf with a free
mind once a fortnight, or half an hour's
intimacy with his wife and a free mind
once a week or so, or a ten minutes' duel
with that daughter of his and a free mind
on an occasional evening! Nay, it may
occur that after forty years of incessant
labour, in answer to an inquiry as to
where the genuine conscious fun comes in,
he has the right only to answer : " Well,
when I have time, I take the dog out for
a walk. I enjoy larking with the dog."

The estimable plain man, with his
3

horror of self-examination, is apt to forget the immediate end of existence in the means. And so much so, that when the first distant end—that of a secure old age —approaches achievement, he is incapable of admitting it to be achieved, and goes on worrying and worrying about the means—from simple habit! And when he does admit the achievement of the desired end, and abandons the means, he has so badly prepared himself to relish the desired end that the mere change kills him! His epitaph ought to read : " Here lies the plain man of common sense, whose life was all means and no end."

A remedy will be worth finding.

CHAPTER II
THE TASTE FOR PLEASURE

CHAPTER II
THE TASTE FOR PLEASURE

I

ONE evening—it is bound to happen in the evening when it does happen—the plain man whose case I endeavoured to analyse in the previous chapter will suddenly explode. The smouldering volcano within that placid and wise exterior will burst forth, and the surrounding country will be covered with the hot lava of his immense hidden grievance. The business day has perhaps been marked by an unusual succession of annoyances, exasperations, disappointments—but he has met them with fine philosophic calm; fatigue has overtaken him—but it has not overcome him; throughout the long ordeal at the office he has remained master of himself, a wondrous example to the young and the foolish. And then some entirely unimportant occurrence—say, an invitation to a golf foursome which his duties forbid him to accept—a trifle, a nothing, comes along and brings about the explosion, in a fashion excessively disconcerting to the onlooker, and he exclaims, acidly, savagely, with a profound pessimism:

" What pleasure do *I* get out of life ? "

And in that single abrupt question (to which there is only one answer) he lays bare the central flaw of his existence.

The onlooker will probably be his wife, and the tone employed will probably imply that she is somehow mysteriously to blame for the fact that his earthly days are not one unbroken series of joyous diversions. He has no pose to keep up

with his wife. And, moreover, if he
really loves her he will find a certain
curious satisfaction in hurting her now
and then, in being wilfully unjust to her,
as he would never hurt or be unjust to a
mere friend. (Herein is one of the mysterious differences between love and affection !) She is alarmed and secretly aghast,
as well she may be. He also is secretly
aghast. For he has confessed a fact
which is an inconvenient fact ; and Anglo-
Saxons have such a horror of inconvenient
facts that they prefer to ignore them even
to themselves. To pretend that things
are not what they are is regarded by
Anglo-Saxons as a proof of strength of
mind and wholesomeness of disposition ;
while to admit that things are indeed
what they are is deemed to be either
weakness or cynicism. The plain man is
incapable of being a cynic ; he feels,
therefore, that he has been guilty of

weakness, and this, of course, makes him very cross.

" Can't something be done ? " says his wife, meaning, " Can't something be done to ameliorate your hard lot ? "

(Misguided creature ! It was the wrong phrase to use. And any phrase would have been the wrong phrase. She ought to have caressed him, for to a caress there is no answer.)

" You know perfectly well that nothing can be done ! " he snaps her up, like a tiger snapping at the fawn. And his eyes, challenging hers, seem to say : " Can I neglect my business ? Can I shirk my responsibilities ? Where would *you* be if I shirked them ? Where would the children be ? What about old age, sickness, death, quarter-day, rates, taxes, and your new hat ? I have to provide for the rainy day and for the future. I am succeeding, moderately ; but let there be no mistake—success means that I must sacrifice present pleasure. Pleasure is all very well for you others, but I——" And then he will finish aloud, with the air of an offended and sarcastic martyr : " Something be done, indeed ! "

She sighs. The domestic scene is over.

Now, he may be honestly convinced that nothing can be done. Let us grant as much. But obviously it suits his pride to assume that nothing can be done. To admit the contrary would be to admit that he was leaving something undone, that he had organized his existence clumsily, even that he had made a fundamental miscalculation in the arrangement of his career. He has confessed to grave dissatisfaction. It behoves him, for the sake of his own dignity and reputation, to be quite sure that the grave dissatisfaction is unavoidable, inevitable, and that the blame for it rests with the scheme of the universe, and not with his particular private scheme. His *rôle* is that of the brave, strong, patient victim of an alleged natural law, by reason of which the present must ever be sacrificed to the future, and he discovers a peculiar miserable delight in the *rôle*. " Miserable " is the right adjective.

Nevertheless, in his quality of a wise plain man, he would never agree that any problem of human conduct, however hard and apparently hopeless, could not be solved by dint of sagacity and ingenuity —provided it was the problem of another person ! He is quite fearfully good at solving the problems of his friends. Indeed, his friends, recognizing this, constantly go to him for advice. If a friend consulted him and said :

" Look here, I'm engaged in an enterprise which will absorb all my energies for three years. It will enable me in the meantime to live and to keep my family, but I shall have scarcely a

moment's freedom of mind. I may have
a little leisure, but of what use is leisure
without freedom of mind? As for
pleasure, I shall simply forget what it
is. My life will be one long struggle.
The ultimate profit is extremely uncertain. It may be fairly good; on
the other hand, it may be nothing at
all."

The plain man, being also blunt, would
assuredly interrupt:

" My dear fellow, what a fool you've
been ! "

Yet this case is in essence the case of
the wise plain man. The chief difference
between the two cases is that the wise
plain man has enslaved himself for about
thirty years instead of three, with naught
but a sheer gambling chance of final
reward ! Not being one of the rare individuals with whom business is a passion,
but just an average plain man, he is

labouring daily against the grain, stultify-
ing daily one part of his nature, on the
supposition that later he will be recom-
pensed. In other words, he is preparing
to live, so that at a distant date he may
be in a condition to live. He has not
effected a compromise between the present
and the future. His own complaint—
" What pleasure do I get out of life ? "—
proves that he is completely sacrificing
the present to the future. And how
elusive is the future ! Like the horizon,
it always recedes. If, when he was thirty,
some one had foretold that at forty-five,
with a sympathetic wife and family and an
increasing income, he would be as far off
happiness as ever, he would have smiled
at the prophecy.

The consulting friend, somewhat nettled
by the plain man's bluntness, might re-
tort :

" I may or may not have been a fool.

That's not the point. The point is that I am definitely *in* the enterprise, and can't get out of it. And there's nothing to be done."

Whereupon the plain man, in an encouraging, enheartening, reasonable tone, would respond :

" Don't say that, my dear chap. Of course, if you're in it, you're in it. But give me all the details. Let's examine the thing. And allow me to tell you that no case that looks bad is as bad as it looks."

It is precisely in this spirit that the plain man should approach his own case. He should say to himself in that reasonable tone which he employs to his friend, and which is so impressive : " Let me examine the thing."

And now the plain man who is reading this and unwillingly fitting the cap will irately protest : " Do you suppose I haven't examined my own case? Do you suppose I don't understand it? I understand it thoroughly. Who should understand it if I don't? I beg to inform you that I know absolutely all about it."

Still the strong probability is that he has not examined it. The strong probability is that he has just lain awake of a night and felt extremely sorry for himself, and at the same time rather proud of his fortitude. Which process does not amount to an examination; it amounts merely to an indulgence. As for knowing absolutely all about it, he has not even noticed that the habit of feeling sorry for himself and proud of his fortitude is slowly growing on him, and tending to become his sole form of joy—a morbid habit and a sickly joy! He is sublimely unaware of that increasing irritability which others discuss behind his back. He has no suspicion that he is balefully affecting the general atmosphere of his home.

Above all, he does not know that he is losing the capacity for pleasure. Indeed, if it were suggested that such a change was going on in him he would be vexed and distressed. He would cry out: " Don't you make any mistake ! I could amuse myself as well as any man, if only I got the chance ! " And yet, how many tens of thousands of plain and (as it is called) successful men have been staggered to discover, when ambition was achieved and the daily yoke thrown off and the direct search for immediate happiness commenced, that the relish for pleasure had faded unnoticed away—proof enough that they had neither examined nor understood themselves ! There is no more ingenuous soul, in affairs of supreme personal importance, than your wise plain man, whom all his friends consult for his sagacity.

Mind, I am not hereby accusing the plain man of total spiritual blindness— any more than I would accuse him of total physical blindness because he cannot see how he looks to others when he walks into a room. For nobody can see all round himself, nor know absolutely all about his own case; and he who boasts that he can is no better than a fool, despite his wisdom; he is not even at the beginning of any really useful wisdom. But I do accuse my plain man of deliberately shutting his eyes, from pride and from sloth. I do say that he might know a great deal more about his case than he actually does know, if only he would cease from pitying and praising himself in the middle of the night, and tackle the business of self-examination in a rational, vigorous, and honest fashion—not in the

4

dark, but in the sane sunlight. And I do further say that a self-examination thus properly conducted might have results which would stultify those outrageous remarks of his to his wife.

III

Few people—in fact, very few people indeed—ever realize the priceless value of the ancient counsel : " Know thyself." It seems so trite, so ordinary. It seems so easy to acquire, this knowledge. Does not every one possess it ? Can it not be got by simply sitting down in a chair and yielding to a mood ? And yet this knowledge is just about as difficult to acquire as a knowledge of Chinese. Certainly nine hundred and ninety-nine people out of a thousand reach the age of sixty before getting the rudiments of it. The majority of us die in almost complete ignorance of it. And none may be said to master it in all its exciting branches. Why, you can choose any of your friends

—the wisest of them—and instantly tell him something glaringly obvious about his own character and actions—and be rewarded for your trouble by an indignantly sincere denial! You had noticed it; all his friends had noticed it. But he had not noticed it. Far from having noticed it, he is convinced that it exists only in your malicious imagination. For example, go to a friend whose sense of humour is notoriously imperfect, and say gently to him : " Your sense of humour is imperfect, my friend," and see how he will receive the information ! So much for the rarity of self-knowledge.

Self-knowledge is difficult because it demands intellectual honesty. It demands that one shall not blink the facts, that one shall not hide one's head in the sand, and that one shall not be afraid of anything that one may happen to see in looking round. It is rare because it demands that one shall always be able to distinguish between the man one thinks one ought to be and the man one actually is. And it is rare because it demands impartial detachment and a certain quality of fine shamelessness—the shamelessness which confesses openly to oneself and finds a legitimate pleasure in confessing. By way of compensation for its difficulty, the pursuit of self-knowledge happens to be one of the most entrancing of all pursuits, as those who have seriously practised it are well aware. Its interest is inexhaustible and grows steadily. Unhappily, the Anglo-Saxon racial temperament is inimical to it. The Latins like it better. To feel its charm one should listen to a highly-cultivated Frenchman analysing himself for the benefit of an intimate companion. Still, even Anglo-Saxons may try it with advantage.

The branch of self-knowledge which is

particularly required for the solution of
the immediate case of the plain man
now under consideration is not a very hard
one. It does not involve the recognition
of crimes or even of grave faults. It is
simply the knowledge of what interests
him and what bores him.

Let him enter upon the first section of
it with candour. Let him be himself.
And let him be himself without shame.
Let him ever remember that it is not a
sin to be bored by what interests others,
or to be interested in what bores others.
Let him in this private inquiry give his
natural instincts free play, for it is precisely the gradual suppression of his
natural instincts which has brought him
to his present pass. At first he will
probably murmur in a fatigued voice
that he cannot think of anything at all
that interests him. Then let him dig
down among his buried instincts. Let

him recall his bright past of dreams, before
he had become a victim imprisoned in
the eternal groove. Everybody has, or
has had, a secret desire, a hidden leaning.
Let him discover what his is, or was—
gardening, philosophy, reading, travel,
billiards, raising animals, training animals,
killing animals, yachting, collecting pic-
tures or postage-stamps or autographs
or snuff-boxes or scalps, astronomy, kite-
flying, house-furnishing, foreign languages,
cards, swimming, diary-keeping, the stage,
politics, carpentry, riding or driving,
music, staying up late, getting up early,
tree-planting, tree-felling, town-planning,
amateur soldiering, statics, entomology,
botany, elocution, children-fancying, cigar-
fancying, wife-fancying, placid domestic
evenings, conjuring, bacteriology, thought-
reading, mechanics, geology, sketching,
bell-ringing, theosophy, his own soul,
even golf. . . .

I mention a few of the ten million directions in which his secret desire may
point or have pointed. I have probably
not mentioned the right direction. But
he can find it. He can perhaps find
several right directions without too much
trouble.

And now he says :

" I suppose you mean me to ' take up '
one of these things ? "

I do, seeing that he has hitherto
neglected so clear a duty. If he had
attended to it earlier, and with perseverance, he would not be in the humiliating
situation of exclaiming bitterly that he
has no pleasure in life.

" But," he resists, " you know perfectly well that I have no time ! "

To which I am obliged to make reply :

" My dear sir, it is not your wife you are
talking to. Kindly be honest with me."

I admit that his business is very exhausting and exigent. For the sake of argument I will grant that he cannot safely give it an instant's less time than he is now giving it. But even so his business does not absorb at the outside more than seventy hours of the hundred and ten hours during which he is wide awake each week. The rest of the time he spends either in performing necessary acts in a tedious way or in performing acts which are not only tedious to him, but utterly unnecessary (for his own hypothesis is that he gets no pleasure out of life)—visiting, dinner-giving, cards, newspaper-reading, placid domestic evenings, evenings out, bar-lounging, sitting aimlessly around, dandifying himself, week-ending, theatres, classical concerts, literature, suburban train-travelling, staying up late, being in the swim, even golf. In whatever manner he is whittling away his leisure, it is the wrong manner, for

the sole reason that it bores him. Moreover, all whittling of leisure is a mistake.
Leisure, like work, should be organized,
and it should be organized in large
pieces.

The proper course clearly is to substitute
acts which promise to be interesting for
acts which have proved themselves to
produce nothing but tedium, and to carry
out the change with brains, in a business
spirit. And the first essential is to recognize that something has definitely to go
by the board.

He protests :

" But I do only the usual things—what
everybody else does ! And then it's time
to go to bed."

The case, however, is *his* case, not
everybody else's case. Why should he
submit to everlasting boredom for the
mere sake of acting like everybody else ?

He continues in the same strain :

" But you are asking me to change my whole life—at my age ! "

Nothing of the sort ! I am only suggesting that he should begin to live.

And then finally he cries :

" It's too drastic. I haven't the pluck ! "

Now we are coming to the real point.

The machinery of his volition, in all directions save one, has been clogged, through persistent neglect, due to over-specialization. His mind needs to be cleared, and it can be cleared—it will clear itself—if regular periods of repose are enforced upon it. As things are, it practically never gets a holiday from business. I do not mean that the plain man is always thinking about his business; but I mean that he is always liable to think about his business, that his business is always present in his mind, even if dormant there, and that at every opportunity, if the mind happens to be inactive, it sits up querulously and insists on attention. The man's mind is indeed

rather like an unfortunate domestic servant who, though not always at work,
is never off duty, never night or day free
from the menace of a damnable electric
bell; and it is as stale as that servant.
His business is capable of ringing the bell
when the man is eating his soup, when he
is sitting alone with his wife on a warm
summer evening, and especially when he
wakes just before dawn to pity and
praise himself.

But he defends the position :

" My business demands much reflection—constant watchfulness."

Well, in the first place, an enterprise
which demands watchfulness day and
night from the same individual is badly
organized, and should be reorganized.
It runs contrary to the common sense of
Nature. And, in the second place, his
defence is insincere. He does not submit
to the eternal preoccupation because he

thinks he ought, but simply because he cannot help it. How often, especially just before the dawn, has he not longed to be delivered from the perfectly futile preoccupation, so that he might go to sleep again—and failed to get free ! How often, in the midst of some jolly gathering, has he not felt secretly desolate because the one tyrannic topic would run round and round in his mind, just like a clockwork mouse, accomplishing no useful end, and making impossible any genuine participation in the gaiety that environs him !

Instead of being necessary to the success of his business, this morbid preoccupation is positively detrimental to his business. He would think much more usefully, more powerfully, more creatively, about his business if during at least thirteen consecutive hours each day he never thought of it at all.

And there is still a further point in this connection. Let him imagine how delightful it must be for the people in the home which he has made, the loving people whom he loves and to whom in theory he is devoting his career, to feel continually that he only sees them obscurely through the haze emanating from his business ! Why—worse !—even when he is sitting with his wife, he and she might as well be communicating with each other across a grille against which a turnkey is standing and listening to every word said ! Let him imagine how flattering for her ! She might be more flattered, at any rate more thrilled, if she knew that instead of thinking about his business he was thinking about another woman. Could he shut the front door every afternoon on his business, the effect would not only be beneficial upon it and upon him, but his wife would smile the warm smile of wisdom justified. Like most women, she has a firmer grasp of the essence of life than the man upon whom she is dependent. She knows with her heart (what he only knows with his brain) that business, politics, and " all that sort of thing " are secondary to real existence, the mere preliminaries of it. She would rejoice, in the blush of the compliment he was paying her, that he had at last begun to comprehend the ultimate values !

So far as I am aware, there is no patent device for suddenly gaining that control of the mind which will enable one to free it from an obsession such as the obsession of the plain man. The desirable end can, however, be achieved by slow degrees, and by an obvious method which contains naught of the miraculous. If the victim of the obsession will deliberately try to think of something else, or to think of nothing at all—every time he catches

himself in the act of thinking about his business out of hours, he certainly will, sooner
or later—probably in about a fortnight
—cure the obsession, or at least get the
upper hand of it. The treatment demands
perseverance, but it emphatically does not
demand an impossibly powerful effort. It
is an affair of trifling pertinacious touches.

It is a treatment easier to practise
during daylight, in company, when dis-
tractions are plentiful, than in the soli-
tude of the night. Triumphantly to battle
with an obsession at night, when the
vitality is low and the egoism intensified,
is extremely difficult. But the small
persistent successes of the day will gradually have their indirect influence on
the night. A great deal can also be done
by simple resolute suggestion. Few persons seem to know—what is, nevertheless,
a fact—that the most effective moment
for making resolves is in the comatose

5

calm which precedes going to sleep. The entire organism is then in a passive state, and more permanently receptive of the imprint of volition than at any other period of the twenty-four hours. If regularly at that moment the man says clearly and imperiously to himself, " I will not allow my business to preoccupy me at home ; I will not allow my business to preoccupy me at home ; I will not allow my business to preoccupy me at home," he will be astonished at the results ; which results, by the way, are reached by subconscious and therefore unperceived channels whose workings we can only guess at.

And when the obsession is beaten, destroyed, he will find himself not merely fortified with the necessary pluck and initiative for importing a new interest into his existence. His instincts of their own accord will be asking for that interest, for they will have been set free.

In choosing a distraction—that is to say, in choosing a rival to his business—he should select some pursuit whose nature differs as much as possible from the nature of his business, and which will bring into activity another side of his character. If his business is monotonous, demanding care and solicitude rather than irregular intense efforts of the brain, then let his distraction be such as will make a powerful call upon his brain. But if, on the other hand, the course of his business runs in crises that string up the brain to its tightest strain, then let his distraction be a foolish and merry one. Many men fall into the error of assuming that their hobbies must be as dignified

and serious as their vocations, though
surely the example of the greatest philo-
sophers ought to have taught them better !
They seem to imagine that they should
continually be improving themselves, in
either body or mind. If they take up a
sport, it is because the sport may improve
their health. And if the hobby is intellectual it must needs be employed to
improve their brain. The fact is that
their conception of self-improvement is
too narrow. In their restricted sense of
the phrase, they possibly don't need
improving ; they possibly are already
improved to the point of being a nuisance
to their fellow-creatures ; possibly what
they need is worsening. In the broad
and full sense of the phrase self-improvement, a course of self-worsening might
improve them. I have known men—and
everybody has known them—who would
approach nearer to perfection if they

could only acquire a little carelessness, a little absent-mindedness, a little illogical-ness, a little irrational and infantile gaiety, a little unscrupulousness in the matter of the time of day. These considerations should be weighed before certain hobbies are dismissed as being unworthy of a plain man's notice.

Then comes the hour of decision, in which the wise plain man should exert all that force of will for which he is famous in his house. For this hour may be of supreme importance—may be the close of one epoch in his life and the beginning of another. The more volitional energy he can concentrate in it, the more likely is he to succeed in the fine enterprise of his own renaissance. He must *resolve* with as much intensity of will as he once put into the resolution which sent him to propose marriage to his wife. And, indeed, he must be ready to treat his hobby somewhat as though it were a woman desired—with splendid and un-calculating generosity. He must shower money on it, and, what is more, he must shower time on it. He must do the thing properly. A hobby is not a hobby until it is glorified, until some real sacrifice has been made for it. If he has chosen a hobby that is costly, both in money and in time, if it is a hobby difficult for a busy and prudent man to follow, all the better. If it demands that his busi-ness shall suffer a little, and that his life-long habits of industry shall seem to be jeopardized, again all the better. For, you know, despite his timid fears, his business will not suffer, and lifelong habits, even good ones, are not easily jeopardized. One of the most precious jewels of advice ever offered to the plain man was that he should acquire indus-trious habits, and then try to lose them !

He will soon find that he cannot lose
them, but the transient struggles against
them will tend always to restore the sane
balance of his nature.

He must deliberately arrange pleasures
for himself in connection with his hobby,
and as often as possible. Once a week at
least his programme should comprise some
item of relaxation to which he can look
forward with impatience because he has
planned it, and because he has compelled
seemingly more urgent matters to give
way to it; and look forward to it he
must, tasting it in advance, enjoying it
twice over ! Thus may the appetite for
pleasure, the ability really to savour it,
be restored—and incidentally kept in good
trim for full use when old age arrives
and he enters the lotus-land. And with
it all, when the hour of enjoyment comes,
he must insist on his mind being free ;
expelling every preoccupation, nonchal-

antly accepting risks like a youth, he must abandon himself to the hour. Let him practise lightheartedness as though it were charity. Indeed, it is charity—to his household, for instance. Ask his household.

He says :

" All this is very dangerous. My friends won't recognize me. I may go too far. I may become an idler and a spendthrift."

Have no fear.

CHAPTER III

THE RISKS OF LIFE

CHAPTER III

THE RISKS OF LIFE

I

By one of those coincidences for which destiny is sometimes responsible, the two very opposite plain men whom I am going to write about were most happily named Mr. Alpha and Mr. Omega; for, owing to a difference of temperament, they stood far apart, at the extreme ends of the scale.

In youth, of course, the differences between them was not fully apparent; such differences seldom are fully apparent in youth. It first made itself felt in a dramatic way, on the evening when Mr. Alpha wanted to go to the theatre and

Mr. Omega didn't. At this period they were both young and both married, and the two couples shared a flat together. Also, they were both getting on very well in their careers, by which is meant that they both had spare cash to rattle in the pockets of their admirably-creased trousers.

" Come to the theatre with us to-night, Omega ? " said Mr. Alpha.

" I don't think we will," said Mr. Omega.

" But we particularly want you to," insisted Mr. Alpha.

" Well, it can't be done," said Mr. Omega.

" Got another engagement ? "

" No."

" Then why won't you come ? You don't mean to tell me you're hard up ? "

" Yes, I do," said Mr. Omega.

" Then you ought to be ashamed of

yourself. What have you been doing with your money lately ? "

" I've taken out a biggish life assurance policy, and the premiums will be a strain. I paid the first yesterday. I'm bled white."

" Holy Moses ! " exclaimed Mr. Alpha, shrugging his shoulders.

The flat was shortly afterwards to let. The exclamation " Holy Moses ! " may be in itself quite harmless, and innocuous to friendship, if it is pronounced in the right, friendly tone. Unfortunately Mr. Alpha used it with a sarcastic inflection, implying that he regarded Mr. Omega as a prig, a fussy old person, a miser, a spoil-sport, and, indeed, something less than a man.

" You can only live your life once," said Mr. Alpha.

And they curved gradually apart. This was in 1893.

Nearly twenty years later—that is to say, not long since—I had a glimpse of Mr. Alpha at a Saturday lunch. Do not imagine that Mr. Alpha's Saturday lunch took place in a miserable garret, amid every circumstance of failure and shame. Success in life has very little to do with prudence. It has a great deal to do with courage, initiative, and individual force, and also it is not unconnected with sheer luck.

Mr. Alpha had succeeded in life, and the lunch at which I assisted took place in a remarkably spacious and comfortable house surrounded by gardens, greenhouses, garages, stables, and all the minions necessary to the upkeep thereof. Mr.

Alpha was a jolly, a kind-hearted, an immensely clever, and a prolific man. I call him prolific because he had five children. There he was, with his wife and the five children ; and they were all enjoying the lunch and themselves to an extraordinary degree. It was a delight to be with them.

It is necessarily a delight to be with people who are intelligent, sympathetic and lively, and who have ample money to satisfy their desires. Somehow you can hear the gold chinking, and the sound is good to the human ear. Even the youngest girl had money in her nice new purse, to do with it as she liked. For Mr. Alpha never stinted. He was generous by instinct, and he wanted everybody to be happy. In fact, he had turned out quite an unusual father. At the same time he fell short of being an absolute angel of acquiescence and compliance.

For instance, his youngest child, a girl, broached the subject of music at that very lunch. She was fourteen, and had shown some of her father's cleverness at a school musical examination. She was rather uplifted about her music.

" Can't I take it up seriously, dad ? " she said, with the extreme gravity of her years.

" Of course," said he. " The better you play, the more we shall all be pleased. Don't you think we deserve some reward for all we've suffered under your piano-practising ? "

She blushed.

" But I mean *seriously*," she insisted.

" Well, my pet," said he, " you don't reckon you could be a star pianist, do you ? Three hundred pounds a concert, and so on ? " And, as she was sitting next to him, he affectionately pinched her delicious ear.

"No," she admitted. "But I could teach. I should like to teach."

"Teach!" He repeated the word in a changed tone. "Teach! What in Heaven's name should you want to teach for? I don't quite see a daughter of mine teaching."

No more was said on the subject.

The young woman and I are on rather confidential terms.

"It is a shame, isn't it?" she said to me afterwards, with feeling.

"Nothing to be done?" I inquired.

"Nothing," said she. "I knew there wasn't before I started. The dad would never *hear* of me earning my own living."

The two elder girls—twins—had no leaning towards music, and no leaning towards anything save family affection and social engagements. They had a grand time, and the grander the time they had the keener was the delight

6

of Mr. Alpha in their paradisaical existence. Truly he was a pearl among
fathers. The children themselves admitted it, and children can judge. The
second son wished to be a painter. Many
a father would have said, " I shall stand
none of this nonsense about painting.
The business is there, and into the business you'll go." But not Mr. Alpha.
What Mr. Alpha said to his second son
amounted to this : " I shall be charmed
for a son of mine to be a painter. Go
ahead. Don't worry. Don't hurry. I
will give you an ample allowance to keep
you afloat through the years of struggle.
You shall not be like other beginners.
You shall have nothing to think of but
your profession. You shall be in a position to wait. Instead of you running
after the dealers, you shall comfortably
bide your time until the dealers run after
you."

This young man of eighteen was precocious and extravagant.

" I say, mater," he said, over the cheese, " can you lend me ten pounds ? "

Mr. Alpha broke in sharply :

" What are you worrying your mother about money for ? You know I won't have it. And I won't have you getting into debt either."

" Well, dad, will you buy a picture from me ? "

" Do me a good sketch of your mother, and I'll give you ten pounds for it."

" Cash in advance ? "

" Yes—on your promise. But understand, no debts."

The eldest son, fitly enough, was in the business. Not, however, too much in the business. He put in time at the office regularly. He was going to be a partner, and the business would ultimately descend

to him. But the business wrinkled not
his brow. Mr. Alpha was quite ready to
assume every responsibility and care.
He had brains and energy enough, and
something considerable over. Enough
over, indeed, to run the house and grounds.
Mrs. Alpha could always sleep soundly
at night secure in the thought that her
husband would smooth away every difficulty for her. He could do all things
so much more efficiently than she could,
were it tackling a cook or a tradesman,
or deciding about the pattern of flowers
in a garden-bed.

At the finish of the luncheon the
painter, who had been meditative, suddenly raised his glass.

" Ladies and gentlemen," he announced,
with solemnity, " I beg to move that
father be and hereby is a brick."

" Carried *nem. con.*," said the eldest
son.

" Loud cheers ! " said the more pert of the twins.

And Mr. Alpha was enchanted with his home and his home-life.

That luncheon was the latest and the most profound of a long series of impressions which had been influencing my mental attitude towards the excellent, the successful, the entirely agreeable Mr. Alpha. I walked home, a distance of some three miles, and then I walked another three miles or so on the worn carpet of my study, and at last the cup of my feelings began to run over, and I sat down and wrote a letter to my friend Alpha. The letter was thus couched :

" MY DEAR ALPHA,

" I have long wanted to tell you something, and now I have decided to give vent to my desire. There are two ways of telling you. I might take the circuitous route by roundabout and gentle phrases, through hints and delicately undulating suggestions, and beneath the soft shadow of flattering cajoleries. Or I might dash straight ahead. The latter is the best, perhaps.

" You are a scoundrel, my dear Alpha. I say it in the friendliest and most brutal manner. And you are not merely a scoundrel—you are the most dangerous sort of scoundrel—the smiling, benevolent scoundrel.

" You know quite well that your house, with all that therein is, stands on the edge of a precipice, and that at any moment a landslip might topple it over into everlasting ruin. And yet you behave as though your house was planted in the midst of a vast and secure plain, sheltered from every imaginable havoc. I speak

metaphorically, of course. It is not a
material precipice that your house stands
on the edge of; it is a metaphorical
precipice. But the perils symbolized by
that precipice are real enough.

"It is, for example, a real chauffeur
whose real wrist may by a single false
movement transform you from the in-
comparable Alpha into an item in the
books of the registrar of deaths. It is a
real microbe who may at this very instant
be industriously planning your swift de-
struction. And it is another real microbe
who may have already made up his or
her mind that you shall finish your days
helpless and incapable on the flat of your
back.

"Suppose you to be dead—what would
happen? You would leave debts, for,
although you are solvent, you are only
solvent because you have the knack of
always putting your hand on money, and

death would automatically make you
insolvent. You are one of those brave,
jolly fellows who live up to their income.
It is true that, in deference to fashion,
you are now insured, but for a trifling
and inadequate sum which would not
yield the hundredth part of your present
income. It is true that there is your
business. But your business would be
naught without you. You are your business. Remove yourself from it, and the
residue is negligible. Your son, left alone
with it, would wreck it in a year through
simple ignorance and clumsiness; for
you have kept him in his inexperience
like a maiden in her maidenhood. You
say that you desired to spare him. Nothing
of the kind. You were merely jealous, of
your authority, and your indispensa-
bility. You desired fervently that all
and everybody should depend on yourself. . . .

" Conceive that three years have passed and that you are in fact dead. You are buried ; you are lying away over there in the cold dark. The funeral is done. The friends are gone. But your family is just as alive as ever. Disaster has not killed it, nor even diminished its vitality. It wants just as much to eat and drink as it did before sorrow passed over it. Look through the sod. Do you see that child there playing with a razor ? It is your eldest son at grips with your business. Do you see that other youngster striving against a wolf with a lead pencil for weapon ? It is your second son. Well, they are males, these two, and must manfully expect what they get. But do you see these four creatures with their hands cut off, thrust out into the infested desert ? They are your wife and your daughters. You cut their hands off. You did it so kindly and persuasively.

And that chiefly is why you are a scoundrel. . . .

" You educated all these women in a false and abominable doctrine. You made them believe, and you forced them to act up to the belief, that money was a magic thing, and that they had a magic power over it. All they had to do was to press a certain button, or to employ a certain pretty tone, and money would flow forth like water from the rock of Moses. And so far as they were concerned money actually did behave in this convenient fashion.

" But all the time you were deceiving them by a conjuring-trick, just as priests of strange cults deceive their votaries. . . . And further, you taught them that money had but one use—to be spent. You may—though by a fluke—have left a quantity of money to your widow, but her sole skill is to spend it. She has heard that there is such a thing as investing money. She tries to invest it. But, bless you, you never said a word to her about that, and the money vanishes now as magically as it once magically appeared in her lap.

"Yes, you compelled all these four women to live so that money and luxury and servants and idleness were absolutely essential to them if their existence was to be tolerable. And what is worse, you compelled them to live so that, deprived of magic money, they were incapable of existing at all, tolerably or intolerably. Either they must expire in misery—after their splendid career with you!—or they must earn existence by smiles and acquiescences and caresses. (For you cut their hands off.) They must beg for their food and raiment. There are different ways of begging.

"But you protest that you did it out

of kindness, and because you wanted
them to have a real good time. My good
Alpha, it is absurd for a man to argue that
he cut off a woman's hands out of kindness. Human beings are so incredulous,
so apt to think evil, that such arguments
somehow fail to carry conviction. I am
fairly credulous myself, but even I decline
to accept the plea. And I say that if
your conduct was meant kindly, it is a
pity that you weren't born cruel. Cruelty
would have been better. Was it out of
kindness that you refused to allow your
youngest to acquire the skill to earn her
own living ? Was it out of kindness that
you thwarted her instinct and filled her
soul with regret that may be eternal ?
It was not. I have already indicated, in
speaking of your son, one of the real
reasons. Another was that you took
pride in having these purely ornamental
and loving creatures about you, and you

would not suffer them to have an interest stronger than their interest in you, or a function other than the function of completing your career and illustrating your success in the world. If the girl was to play the piano, she was to play it in order to perfect your home and minister to your pleasure and your vanity, and for naught else. You got what you wanted, and you infamously shut your eyes to the risks.

" I hear you expostulate that you didn't shut your eyes to the risks, and that there will always be risks, and that it is impossible to provide fully against all of them.

" Which is true, or half true, and the truth or half-truth of the statement only renders your case the blacker, O Alpha ! Risks are an inevitable part of life. They are part of the fine savour and burden of life, and without the sense of them life is flat and tasteless. And yet you feigned to your women that risk was eliminated from the magic world in which you had put them. You deliberately deprived them of the most valuable factor in existence—genuine responsibility. You made them ridiculous in the esteem of all persons with a just perception of values. You slowly bled them of their self-respect. Had you been less egotistic, they might have been happier, even during your lifetime. Your wife would have been happier had she been permitted or compelled to feel the weight of the estate and to share understandingly the anxieties of your wonderful business. Your girls would have been happier had they been cast forcibly out of the magic world into the real world for a few hours every day during a few years in order to learn its geography, and its customs, and the terms on which food and raiment and respect can be obtained in it, and the ability to obtain them. And so would you have been happier, fool! You sent your girls on the grand tour, but you didn't send them into the real world.

" Alpha, the man who cuts off another man's hands is a ruffian. The man who cuts off a woman's hands is a scoundrel. There is no excuse for him—none whatever. And the kinder he is the worse he is. I repeat that you are the worst sort of scoundrel. Your family mourns you, and every member of it says what an angel of a father you were. But you were a scoundrel all the same. And at heart every member of the family knows it and admits it. Which is rather distressing. And there are thousands just like you, Alpha. Yes, even in England there are tens of thousands just like you. . . .

" But you aren't dead yet. I was

only asking you to conceive that you were.

"Believe me, my dear Alpha,

"Yours affectionately."

A long and violent epistle perhaps. You inquire in what spirit Alpha received it. The truth is, he never did receive it.

You naturally assume that before the letter could reach him Alpha had been mortally struck down by apoplexy, double pneumonia, bullet, automobile, or some such enemy of joy, and that all the dreadful things which I had foreseen might happen did in fact happen, thus proving once more what a very wise friend I was, and filling me with justifiable pride in my grief. But it was not so. Alpha was not struck down, nor did his agreeable house topple over the metaphorical precipice. According to poetical justice he ought to have been struck down, just to serve him right, and as a warning to others—only he was not. Not merely the wicked, but the improvident and the

negligent, often flourish like the green
bay tree, and they keep on flourishing,
and setting wisdom and righteousness
at defiance in the most successful manner.
Which, indeed, makes the life of a phil-
osopher and sagacious adviser extremely
difficult and ungrateful.

Alpha never received my letter because
I never sent it. There are letters which
one writes, not to send, but to ease one's
mind. This letter was one of them. It
would not have been proper to dispatch
such a letter. Moreover, in the duties of
friendship, as distinguished from the pleasures of friendship, speech is better,
bolder, surer than writing. When two
friends within hailing distance of each
other get to exchanging epistles in order
to settle a serious difference of opinion,
the peril to their friendship is indeed
grave; and the peril is intensified when
one of them has adopted a superior moral

attitude—as I had. The letters gro
longer and longer, ruder and ruder, and
the probability of the friendship surviving
grows ever rapidly less and less. It is—
usually, though not always—a mean act
to write what you have not the pluck to
say.

So I just kept the letter as a specimen
of what I could do—if I chose—in the
high *rôle* of candid friend.

I said to myself that I would take the
first favourable occasion to hint to Mr.
Alpha how profoundly, etc., etc.

The occasion arrived sooner than I had
feared. Alpha had an illness. It was not
alarming, and yet it was sufficiently
formidable. It began with colitis, and
ended with appendicitis and an operation. Soon after Alpha had risen from
his bed and was cheerfully but somewhat
feebly about again I met him at a club.
He was sitting in an arm-chair in one of

the huge bay-windows of the club, and gazing with bright interest upon the varied spectacle of the street. The occasion was almost ideal. I took the other arm-chair in the semicircle of the window. I saw at once by his careless demeanour that his illness had taught him nothing, and I determined with all my notorious tact and persuasiveness to point a moral for him.

And just as I was clearing my throat to begin he exclaimed, with a jerk of the elbow and a benevolently satiric smile :

" See that girl ? "

A plainly-dressed young woman carrying a violin-case crossed the street in front of our window.

" I see her," said I. " What about her ? "

" That's Omega's second daughter."

" Oh, Omega," I murmured. " Haven't seen him for ages. What's he doing with

himself ?   Do you ever meet him nowadays ? "

Said Mr. Alpha :

" I happened to dine with him—it was
chiefly on business—a couple of days
before I fell ill. Remarkably strange
cove, Omega—remarkably strange."

" Why ?   How ?   And what's the matter with the cove's second daughter,
anyway ? "

" Well," said Alpha, " it's all of a
piece—him and his second daughter and
the rest of the family. Funny case. It
ought to interest you. Omega's got a
mania."

" What mania ? "

" Not too easy to describe.   Call it the
precaution mania."

" The   precaution   mania ?   What's
that ? "

" I'll tell you."

And he told me,

V

"Odd thing," said Alpha, "that I should have been at Omega's just as I was sickening for appendicitis. He's great on appendicitis, is Omega."

"Has he had it?"

"Not he! He's never had anything. But he informed me that before he went to Mexico last year he took the precaution of having his appendix removed, lest he *might* have acute appendicitis in some wild part of the country where there *might* be no doctor just handy for an operation. He's like that, you know. I believe if he had his way there wouldn't be an appendix left in the entire family. He's inoculated against everything. They're all inoculated against everything. And he keeps an elaborate medicine-

chest in his house, together with elaborate
typewritten instructions wnich he forced
his doctor to give him—in case anything
awful should happen suddenly. Omega
has only to read those instructions, and
he could stitch a horrible wound, tie up
a severed artery, or make an injection of
morphia or salt water. He has a ther-
mometer in every room and one in each
bath. Also burglar-alarms at all doors
and windows, and fire-extinguishers on
every floor. But that's nothing. You
should hear about his insurances. Of
course, he's insured his life and the lives
of the whole family of them. He's insured
against railway accidents and all other
accidents, and against illness. The fidelity
of all his clerks is insured. He's insured
against burglary, naturally. Against fire,
too. And against loss of rent through
fire. His plate-glass is insured. His
bunch of keys is insured. He's insured

against employers' liability.   He's insured
against war.   He's insured against loss
of business profits.   The interest on his
mortgage   securities   is   insured.   His
wretched little automobile is insured.   I
do believe he was once insured against
the eventuality of twins."

"He must feel safe," I said.

"Not the least bit in the world,"
replied Alpha.   "Life is a perfect burden
to him.   That wouldn't matter so much
if he didn't make it a perfect burden
to all his family as well.   They've all got
to be prepared against the worst happen-
ing.   If he fell down dead his wife would
know just what to do.   She knows all
the details of his financial position exactly.
She has to ;   he sees to that.   He keeps
her up to date in them every day.   And
she has to show him detailed accounts of
the house as though it was a business
undertaking,   because he's so afraid of

her being left helpless and incapable.
She just has to understand that ' life is
real, life is earnest,' and death more so.

"Then the children! They're all insured, of course. Each of the girls has
to take charge of the house in turn. And
they must all earn their own living—in
case papa fell down dead. Take that
second daughter. She hates music, but
she has a certain mechanical facility with
the fiddle, and so she must turn it into
coin, in order to be on the safe side.
Her instincts are for fine clothes, idleness,
and responsibility. She'd take the risks
cheerfully enough if he'd let her. But
he won't. So she's miserable. I think
they all are more or less."

"But still," I put in, "to feel the burden
of life is not a bad thing for people's
characters."

"Perhaps not," said Alpha. "But to
be crushed under a cartload of bricks

isn't likely to do one much good, is it?
Why, Omega's a wealthy man, and d'you
know, he must live on about a third of
his income. The argument is, as usual,
that he's liable to fall down dead—and
insurance companies are only human—and
anyhow, old age must be amply provided
for. And then all his securities might fall
simultaneously. And lastly, as he says,
you never know what may happen. Ugh!"

"Has anything happened up to now?"

"Oh, yes. An appalling disaster. His
drawing-room hearthrug caught fire six
years ago and was utterly ruined. He
got two pounds five out of the insurance
company for that, and was ecstatically
delighted about it for three weeks.
Nothing worse ever will happen to Omega.
His business is one of the safest in the
country. His constitution is that of a
crocodile or a parrot. And he's as cute
as they make 'em."

" And I suppose you don't envy him ? "

" I don't," said Alpha.

" Well," I ventured, " let me offer you a piece of advice. Never travel in the same train with Mr. Omega."

" Never travel in the same train with him ? Why not ? "

" Because if there were a railway accident, and you were both killed on the spot, the world might draw comparisons between the effect on your family and the effect on his, and your family wouldn't like it."

We remained silent for a space, and the silence was dramatic. Nervously, I looked out of the window.

At length Alpha said :

" I suppose there *is* such a thing as the happy medium."

" Good-bye, Alpha." I rose abruptly. " Sorry, but I've got to go at once."

And I judiciously departed.

CHAPTER IV

IN HER PLACE

CHAPTER IV

IN HER PLACE

I

THE plain man is not always mature and successful, as I have hitherto regarded him. He may be unsuccessful in a worldly sense; but from my present point of view I do not much care whether he is unsuccessful or successful in that sense. I know that plain men are seldom failures; their very plainness saves them from the alarming picturesqueness of the abject failure. On the other hand, I care greatly whether the plain man is mature or immature, old or young. I should prefer to catch him young. But he is difficult to catch young. The fact is that, just as he is seldom a failure, so he is seldom young. He becomes plain only with years. In youth, even in the thirties, he has fanciful capricious qualities which prevent him from being classed with the average sagacious plain man. He slowly loses these inconvenient qualities, and develops into part of the backbone of the nation. And then it is too late to tell him that he is not perfect, simply because he has forgotten to cultivate the master quality of all qualities—namely, imagination. For imagination must be cultivated early, and it is just the quality that these admirable plain men lack.

By imagination I mean the power to conceive oneself in a situation which one is not actually in; for instance, in another person's place. It is among the sardonic humours of destiny that imagination, while positively dangerous in an ill-balanced mind and of the highest value in a well-balanced mind, is to be found rather in the former than in the latter. And anyhow, the quality is rare in Anglo-Saxon races, which are indeed both afraid and ashamed of it.

And yet could the plain, the well-balanced Anglo-Saxon male acquire it, what a grand world we should live in! The most important thing in the world would be transformed. The most important thing in the world is, ultimately, married life, and the chief practical use of the quality of imagination is to ameliorate married life. But who in England or America (or elsewhere) thinks of it in that connection? The plain man considers that imagination is all very well for poets and novelists. Blockhead! Yes, despite my high esteem for him, I will apply to him the Johnsonian term of abuse. Blockhead! Imagination is super-eminently for himself, and was beyond

8

doubt invented by Providence in order that the plain man might chiefly exercise it in the plain, drudging dailiness of married life. The day cometh, if tardily, when he will do so.

These reflections have surged up in my brain as I contemplate the recent case of my acquaintance, Mr. Omicron, and they are preliminary to a study of that interesting case. Scarce a week ago Omicron was sitting in the Omicron drawing-room alone with Mrs. Omicron. It was an average Omicron evening. Omicron is aged thirty-two. He is neither successful nor unsuccessful, and no human perspicacity can say whether twenty years hence he will be successful or unsuccessful. But anybody can see that he is already on the way to be a plain, well-balanced man. Somewhat earlier than usual he is losing the fanciful capricious qualities and settling down into the stiff backbone of the nation.

Conversation was not abundant.

Said Mrs. Omicron suddenly, with an ingratiating accent :

" What about that ring that I was to have ? "

There was a pause, in which every muscle of the man's body, and especially the facial muscles, and every secret fibre of his soul, perceptibly stiffened. And then Omicron answered, curtly, rebut-tingly, reprovingly, snappishly, finish-ingly :

" I don't know."

And took up his newspaper, whose fragile crackling wall defended him from attack every bit as well as a screen of twelve-inch armour-plating.

The subject was dropped.

It had endured about ten seconds. But those ten seconds marked an epoch in Omicron's career as a husband—and he knew it not. He knew it not, but the whole of his conjugal future had hung evenly in the balance during those ten seconds, and then slid slightly but definitely—to the wrong side.

Of course, there was more in the affair than appeared on the surface. At dinner the otherwise excellent leg of mutton had proved on cutting to be most noticeably underdone. Now, it is a monstrous shame that first-class mutton should be wasted through inefficient cookery; with third-class mutton the crime might have been deemed less awful. Moreover, four days previously another excellent dish had been rendered unfit for masculine consumption by precisely the same inefficiency or gross negligence, or whatever one likes to call it. Nor was that all. The coffee had been thin, feeble, uninteresting. The feminine excuse for this last diabolic iniquity had been that the kitchen at the last moment had discovered itself to be short of coffee. An entirely commonplace episode! Yes, but it is out of commonplace episodes that martyrs are made, and Omicron had been made a martyr. He, if none else, was fully aware that evening that he was a martyr. And the woman had selected just that evening to raise the question of rings, gauds, futile ornamentations! He had said little. But he had stood for the universal husband, and in Mrs. Omicron he saw the universal wife.

III

His reflections ran somewhat thus :

" Surely a simple matter to keep enough coffee in the house ! A schoolgirl could do it ! And yet they let themselves run short of coffee ! I ask for nothing out of the way. I make no inordinate demands on the household. But I do like good coffee. And I can't have it ! Strange ! As for that mutton—one would think there was no clock in the kitchen. One would think that nobody had ever cooked a leg of mutton before. How many legs of mutton have they cooked between them in their lives ? Scores ; hundreds ; I dare say thousands. And yet it hasn't yet dawned on them that a leg of mutton of a certain weight requires

a certain time for cooking, and that if
it is put down late one of two things must
occur—either it will be undercooked or
the dinner will be late! Simple enough!
Logical enough! Four women in the
house [three servants and the wicked,
negligent Mrs. Omicron], and yet they
must needs waste a leg of mutton through
nothing but gross carelessness! It isn't
as if it hadn't happened before! It isn't
as if I hadn't pointed it out! But women
are amateurs. All women are alike. All
housekeeping is amateurish. She (Mrs.
Omicron, the criminal) has nothing in
this world to do but run the house—and
see how she runs it! No order! No
method! Has she ever studied housekeeping scientifically? Not she! Does
she care? Not she! If she had any
real sense of responsibility, if she had the
slightest glimmering of her own short-
comings, she wouldn't have started on

the ring question. But there you are!
She only thinks of spending, and titivating
herself. I wish she had to do a little
earning. She'd find out a thing or two
then. She'd find out that life isn't all
moonstones and motor-cars. Ring, indeed! It's the lack of tact that annoys
me. I am an ill-used man. All husbands
are ill-used men. The whole system
wants altering. However, I must keep
my end up. And I will keep my end up.
Ring, indeed! No tact!"

He fostered a secret fury. And he
enjoyed fostering it. There was exag-
geration in these thoughts, which, he
would admit next day, were possibly too
sweeping in their scope. But he would
maintain the essential truth of them.
He was not really and effectively furious
against Mrs. Omicron; he did not, as a
fact, class her with forgers and drunken
chauffeurs; indeed, the fellow loved her

in his fashion. But he did pass a mature judgment against her. He did wrap up his grudge in cotton-wool and put it in a drawer and examine it with perverse pleasure now and then. He did increase that secretion of poison which weakens the social health of nine hundred and ninety-nine in a thousand married lives —however delightful they may be. He did render more permanent a noxious habit of mind. He did appreciably and doubly and finally impair the conjugal happiness—for it must not be forgotten that in creating a grievance for himself he also gave his wife a grievance. He did, in fine, contribute to the general mass of misunderstanding between sex and sex.

If he is reading this, as he assuredly is, Mr. Omicron will up and exclaim :

" My wife a grievance ! Absurd ! The facts are incontrovertible. What grievance can she have ? "

The grievance that Mr. Omicron, be-
coming every day more and more the
plain man, is not exercising imagination
in the very field where it is most needed.

What is a home, Mr. Omicron ? You
reply that a home is a home. You have
always had a home. You were born in
one. With luck you will die in one.
And you have never regarded a home as
anything but a home. Your leading idea
has ever been that a home is emphatically
not an office nor a manufactory. But
suppose you were to unscale your eyes—
that is to say, use your imagination—and
try to see that a home, in addition to being
a home, is an office and manufactory for
the supply of light, warmth, cleanliness,
ease, and food to a given number of
people ? Suppose you were to allow it to
occur to you that a home emphatically *is*
an organization similar to an office and
manufactory—and an extremely com-

plicated and delicate one, with many diverse departments, functioning under extremely difficult conditions ? For thus it in truth is. Could you once accomplish this feat of the imaginative faculty, you would never again say, with that disdainful accent of yours : " Mrs. Omicron has nothing in the world to do but run the house." For really it would be just as clever for her to say : " Mr. Omicron has nothing in the world to do but run the office."

I admit heartily that Mrs. Omicron is not perfect. She ought to be, of course ; but she, alas ! falls short of the ideal. Yet in some details she can and does show the way to that archangel, her husband. When her office and manufactory goes wrong, you, Mr. Omicron, are righteously indignant and superior. You majestically wonder that with four women in the house, etc., etc. But when you come home and

complain that things are askew in your
masculine establishment, and that a period
of economy must set in, does she say to
you with scorn : " Don't dare to mention
coffee to-night. I really wonder that with
fourteen (or a hundred and forty) grown
men in your establishment you cannot
produce an ample and regular income " ?
No ; she makes the best of it. She is
sympathetic. And you, Mr. Omicron,
would be excessively startled and wounded
if she were not sympathetic. Put your
imagination to work, and you will see
how interesting are these comparisons.

She is an amateur at her business, you say. Well, perhaps she is. But who brought her up to be an amateur ? Are you not content to carry on the ancient tradition ? As you meditate, and you often do meditate, upon that infant daughter of yours now sleeping in her cot, do you dream of giving her a scientific education in housekeeping, or do you dream of endowing her with the charms that music and foreign languages and physical grace can offer ? Do you in your mind's eye see her cannily choosing beef at the butcher's, or shining for your pleasure in the drawing-room ?

And then Mrs. Omicron is, perhaps, not so much of an amateur as you assume.

People learn by practice. Is there any reason in human nature why a complex machine such as a house may be worked with fewer breakdowns than an office or manufactory ? Harness your imagination once more, and transfer to your house the multitudinous minor catastrophes that happen in your office. Be sincere, and admit that the efficiency of the average office is naught but a pretty legend. A mistake or negligence or forgetfulness in an office is remedied and forgotten. Mrs. Omicron—my dear Mr. Omicron—never hears of it. Not so with Mrs. Omicron's office, as your aroused imagination will tell you. Mrs. Omicron's parlourmaid's duster fails to make contact with one small portion of the hall-table. Mr. Omicron walks in, and his godlike glance drops instantly on the dusty place, and Mr. Omicron ejaculates sardonically : " H'm ! Four women in the house, and they can't even keep the hall-table respectable ! "

Mr. Omicron forgets a letter at the bottom of his unanswered-letter basket, and a week later an excited cable arrives from overseas, and that cable demands another cable. No real harm has been done. Two pounds spent on cables have cured the ill. Mrs. Omicron, preoccupied with a rash on the back of the neck of Miss Omicron before-mentioned, actually comes back from town without having ordered the mutton. In the afternoon she realizes her horrid sin and rushes to the telephone. The butcher reassures her. He swears the desired leg shall arrive. But do you see that boy dallying at the street corner with his mate ? He carries the leg of mutton, and he carries also, though he knows it not nor cares, the reputation and happiness of Mrs. Omicron. He is late. As you yourself remarked, Mr. Omicron, if a leg of mutton is put down late to roast, one of two things must occur—either it will be under-cooked or the dinner will be late.

Now, if housekeeping was as simple as officekeeping, Mrs. Omicron would smile in tranquillity at the *contretemps*, and say to herself : " Never mind, I shall pay the late-posting fee—that will give me an extra forty minutes." *You* say that, Mr. Omicron, about your letters, when you happen to have taken three hours for lunch and your dictation of corre-spondence is thereby postponed. Only there is no late-posting fee in Mrs. Omi-cron's world. If Mrs. Omicron flung twopence at you when you came home, and informed you that dinner would be forty minutes late and that she was paying the fee, what, Mr. Omicron, would be your state of mind ?

And your imagination, now very alert,

9

will carry you even farther than this, Mr. Omicron, and disclose to you still more fearful difficulties which Mrs. Omicron has to face in the management of her office or manufactory. Her staff is uneducated, less educated even than yours. And her staff is universally characterized by certain peculiarities of mentality. For example, her staff will never, never, never, come and say to her : " Please, ma'am, there is only enough coffee left for two days." No! Her staff will placidly wait forty-eight hours, and then come at seven p.m. and say : " Please, ma'am, there isn't enough coffee——" And worse ! You, Mr. Omicron, can say roundly to a clerk : " Look here, if this occurs again I shall fling you into the street." You are aware, and he is aware, that a hundred clerks are waiting to take his place. On the other hand, a hundred mistresses are waiting to take the place of Mrs. Omicron with regard to her cook. Mrs. Omicron has to do as best she can. She has to speak softly and to temper discipline, because the supply of domestic servants is unequal to the demand. And there is still worse. The worst of all, the supreme disadvantage under which Mrs. Omicron suffers, is that most of her errors, lapses, crimes, directly affect a man in the stomach, and the man is a hungry man.

Mr. Omicron, your imagination, now feverishly active, will thus demonstrate to you that your wife's earthly lot is not the velvet couch that you had unimaginatively assumed it to be, and that, indeed, you would not change places with her for a hundred thousand a year. Your attitude towards her human limitations will be modified, and the general mass of misunderstanding between sex and sex will tend to diminish.

(And if even yet your attitude is not modified, let your imagination dwell for a few instants on the extraordinary number of bad and expensive hotels with which you are acquainted—managed, not by amateurish women, but by professional men. And on the obstinate mismanagement of the commissariat of your own club—of which you are continually complaining to members of the house-committee.)

I pass to another aspect of Mr. Omicron's private reflections consequent upon
Mrs. Omicron's dreadful failure of tact
in asking him about the ring after the
mutton had proved to be underdone and
the coffee to be inadequate. "She only
thinks of spending," reflected Mr. Omicron, resentfully. A more or less true
reflection, no doubt, but there would
have been a different colour to it if Mr.
Omicron had exercised the greatest of
his faculties. Suppose you were to unscale your eyes, Mr. Omicron—that is to
say, use your imagination—and try to
see that so far as finance is concerned your
wife's chief and proper occupation in life
is to spend. Conceive what you would

say if she announced one morning: "Henry, I am sick of spending. I am going out into the world to earn." Can you not hear yourself employing a classic phrase about " the woman's sphere " ? In brief, there would occur an altercation and a shindy.

Your imagination, once set in motion, will show you that your conjugal existence is divided into two great departments—the getting and the spending departments. Wordsworth chanted that in getting and spending we lay waste our powers. We could not lay waste our powers in a more satisfying manner. The two departments, mutually indispensable, balance each other. You organized them. You made yourself the head of one and your wife the head of the other. You might, of course, have organized them otherwise. It was open to you in the Hottentot style to decree

that your wife should do the earning
while you did the spending. But for
some mysterious reason this arrangement
did not appeal to you, and you accordingly
go forth daily to the office and return
therefrom with money. The theory of
your daily excursion is firmly based in
the inherent nature of things. The theory
is the fundamental cosmic one that money
is made in order that money may be
spent—either at once or later. Even the
miser conforms to this theory, for he only
saves in obedience to the argument that
the need of spending in the future may
be more imperious than is the need of
spending at the moment.

The whole of your own personal activity
is a mere preliminary to the activity of
Mrs. Omicron. Without hers, yours would
be absurd, ridiculous, futile, supremely
silly. By spending she completes and
justifies your labour ; she crowns your

life by spending. You married her so that she might spend. You wanted someone to spend, and it was understood that she should fill the situation. She was brought up to spend, and you knew that she was brought up to spend. Spending is her vocation. And yet you turn round on her and complain, " She only thinks of spending."

"Yes," you say, " but there is such a thing as moderation." There is; I admit it. The word " extravagance " is no idle word in the English language. It describes a quality which exists. Let it be an axiom that Mrs. Omicron is human. Just as the tendency to get may grow on you, until you become a rapacious and stingy money-grubber, so the tendency to spend may grow on her. One has known instances. A check-action must be occasionally employed. Agreed! But, Mr. Omicron, you should choose a time and a tone for employing it other than you chose on this evening that I have described. A man who mixes up jewelled rings with underdone mutton and feeble coffee is a clumsy man.

Exercise your imagination to put yourself in the place of Mrs. Omicron, and you will perceive that she is constantly in the highly delicate difficulty of having to ask for money, or at any rate of having to suggest or insinuate that money should be given to her. It is her right and even her duty to ask for money, but the foolish, illogical creature—like most women, even those with generous and polite husbands—regards the process as a little humiliating for herself. You, Mr. Omicron, have perhaps never asked for money. But your imagination will probably be able to make you feel how it feels to ask for money. A woman whose business in life it is to spend money which she does not and cannot earn may sometimes have to face a refusal when she asks for money. But there is one thing from which she ought to be absolutely and eternally safe —and that is a snub.

VI

And finally, in his reflections as an ill-used man tied for life to a woman who knows not tact, Mr. Omicron asserted further that Mrs. Omicron only thought of spending and titivating herself. To assert that she only thought of spending did not satisfy his spleen; he must add "titivating herself." He would admit, of course, that she did as a fact sometimes think of other matters, but still he would uphold the gravamen of his charge. And yet—excellent Omicron!—you have but to look the truth in the face—as a plain common-sense man will—and to use your imagination, in order to perceive that there really is no gravamen in the charge.

Why did you insist on marrying Mrs.

Omicron ? She had the reputation of
being a good housekeeper (as girls go) ;
she was a serious girl, kind-hearted, of
irreproachable family, having agreeable
financial expectations, clever, well-edu-
cated, good-tempered, pretty. But the
truth is that you married her for none
of these attributes. You married her
because you were attracted to her ; and
what attracted you was a mysterious,
never-to-be-defined quality about her—
an effluence, an emanation, a lurking
radiance, an entirely enigmatic charm.
In the end " charm " is the one word
that even roughly indicates that element
in her personality which caused you to
lose your head about her. A similar
phenomenon is to be observed in all
marriages of inclination. A similar phenomenon is at the bottom of most social
movements. Why, the Men's League for
Women's Suffrage itself certainly came

into being through the strange workings
of that same phenomenon ! You married
Mrs. Omicron doubtless because she was
" suitable," but her " suitability," for
you, consisted in the way she breathed,
the way she crossed a room, a transient
gesture, a vibration in her voice, a blush,
a glance, the curve of an arm—nothing,
nothing—and yet everything !

You may condescend towards this
quality of hers, Mr. Omicron—you may
try to dismiss it as " feminine charm,"
and have done with it. But you cannot
have done with it. And the fact will ever
remain that you are incapable of supply-
ing it yourself, with all your talents and
your divine common sense. You are an
extremely wise and good man, but you
cannot ravish the senses of a roomful of
people by merely walking downstairs, by
merely throwing a shawl over your shoulders, by a curious depression in the corner

of one cheek. This gift of grace is not yours. Wise as you are, you will be still wiser if you do not treat it disdainfully. It is among the supreme things in the world. It has made a mighty lot of history, and not improbably will make some more—even yours.

You were not the only person aware of the formidable power (for formidable it was) which she possessed over you. She, too, was aware of it, and is still. She knows that when she exists in a particular way, she will produce in your existence a sensation which, though fleeting, you prefer to all other sensations— a sensation unique. And this quality by which she disturbs and enchants you is her main resource in the adventure of life. Shall she not cherish this quality, adorn it, intensify it? On the contrary, you well know that you would be very upset and amazed if Mrs. Omicron were to show signs of neglecting this quality of hers which yearns for rings. And, if you have ever entered a necktie-shop and been dazzled by the spectacle of a fine necktie into " hanging expense "—if you have been through this wondrous experience, your imagination, duly prodded, will enable you to put yourself into Mrs. Omicron's place when she mentions the subject of rings. " Titivating herself " ? Good heavens, she is helping the very earth to revolve ! And you smote the defenceless creature with a lethal word—because the butcher's boy dallied at a street-corner !

You insinuate that one frail hand may carry too many rings. You reproduce your favourite word " moderation." Mr. Omicron, I take you. I agree as to the danger. But if Mrs. Omicron is human, let us also bear in mind the profound truth that not one of us is more human than another.

PRINTED BY
HAZELL, WATSON AND VINEY, LD.
LONDON AND AYLESBURY.